Violet and Her Tablet

Go to the Farm

To my daughters and all the children who enjoy playing outside-
Eleanor Javorsek

To all the children who refuse to be tablet zombies-
Kathryn Harper

Library of Congress Control Number: 2020909671

Names: Javorsek, Eleanor, 1982- author. | Harper, Kathryn, 1955- illustrator.

Title: Violet and her tablet go to the farm / written by: Eleanor Javorsek ; illustrated by: Kathryn Harper.

Description: La Plata, MD : Eleanor Javorsek, [2020] | Audience: Juvenile. | Summary: Violet thinks she can learn everything from her tablet. Join Violet as she goes on a field trip to a farm, where she learns that some things are better to experience in person.--Publisher.

Identifiers: ISBN: 978-735105703 (hardcover) | 978-1735105710 (paperback) | 978-1735105727 (ebook) | LCCN: 2020909671

Subjects: LCSH: Tablet computers--Juvenile fiction. | Farms--Juvenile fiction. | Farm life--Juvenile fiction. | Families--Juvenile fiction. | Experience in children--Juvenile fiction. | Internet and children--Juvenile fiction. | Internet--Social aspects--Juvenile fiction. | Digital media--Social aspects--Juvenile fiction. | Cyberspace--Psychological aspects--Juvenile fiction. | Interpersonal relations in children--Juvenile fiction. | Children--Life skills guides. | CYAC: Tablet computers--Fiction. | Farms--Fiction. | Farm life--Fiction. | Families--Fiction. | Experience--Fiction. | Internet--Social aspects--Fiction. | Digital media--Fiction. | Interpersonal relations--Fiction. | Conduct of life--Fiction. | LCGFT: Picture books.

Classification: LCC: PZ7.1.J392 V56 2020 | DDC: [E]--dc23

Violet and Her Tablet Go to the Farm

Written By: Eleanor Javorsek

Illustrated By: Kathryn Harper

Violet loved her tablet. There were so many amazing things she could do on her tablet! She could play games, watch movies, read books, and look up interesting facts. Violet decided she only needed her tablet to learn new things.

At school, Violet's teacher announced that the class was going on a field trip to a farm. All the other kids jumped for joy.

Violet stayed in her seat looking bored.

"Violet, aren't you excited to go?" asked her teacher.

"Not really," said Violet, "I can learn everything I need right here." She searched the word 'farm' on her tablet. "See, it says that a farm is an area of land used to grow plants and raise animals."

Later that night, Violet's mother told her she must go on the field trip, because she might get to try something new. Violet said she would only go if she could take her tablet. She didn't understand why she even had to go, since she could look up all the plants and animal facts she wanted. There was nothing for her to learn by going to the farm.

The school bus pulled up to Flying J. Farm. Fields with rows of green plants were surrounded by long white fences. A red barn had animals running all around.

Violet's teacher introduced the class to a farmer named Ms. Fannie, who was carrying some fresh vegetables picked from the fields. Ms. Fannie told them she was their guide for the day.

First, Ms. Fannie took them to see the chickens. She started telling the students how they collect and sell the eggs at the farm store. The eggs were found in hen boxes in the coop. Violet stepped back from the group to look up 'chickens' on her tablet. She was busy looking at her screen.

Just then, a hen with three baby chicks walked up to the chicken coop. All the other students said, "Awe, they're so cute!"

Violet looked up from her screen and asked, "What is cute?"

"One of the hens had three little chicks with her! They just walked into the coop! Didn't you see them?" replied one of the little boys in her class.

Violet had been looking at her screen, so she missed out on seeing the baby chicks.

As they continued on, Ms. Fannie started telling the class about how the farm makes butter to sell with the cow's milk. People came from miles around to get fresh eggs, milk, butter, and produce at The Flying J. Farm Store.

Violet led the class line as they kept walking towards the cow pens.

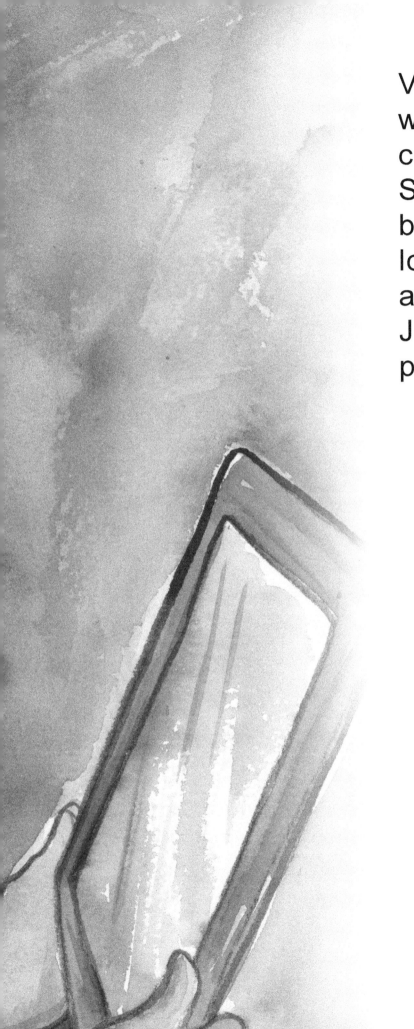

Violet decided she wanted to learn about cows from her tablet. She moved to the back of the class to look up cow facts, and a student named James took her place.

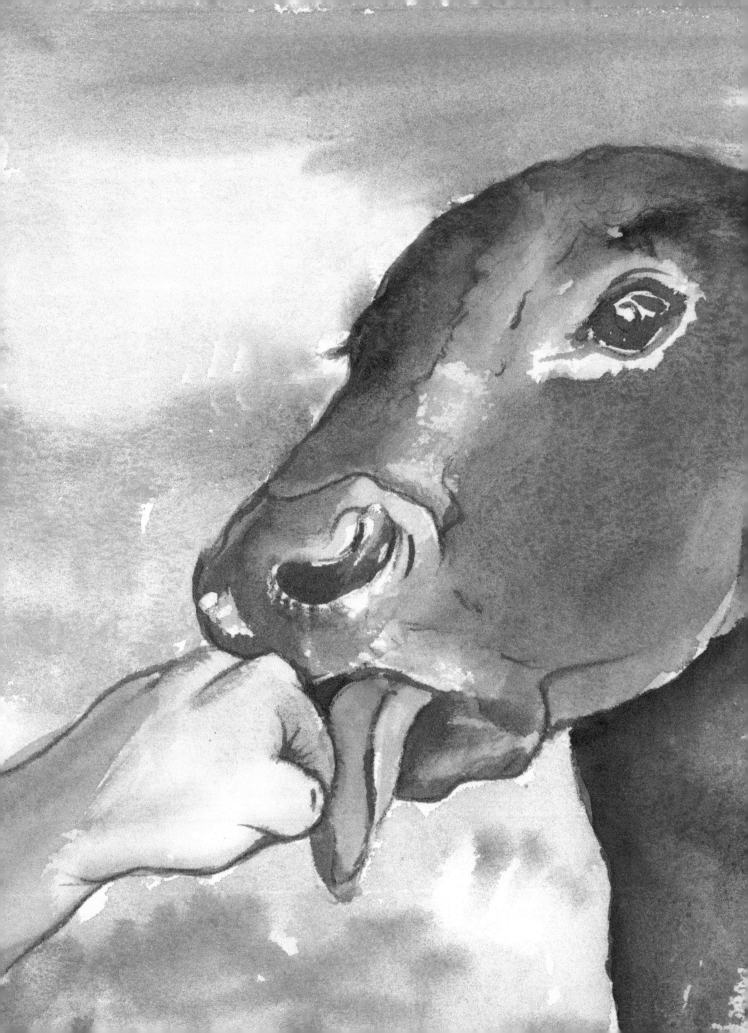

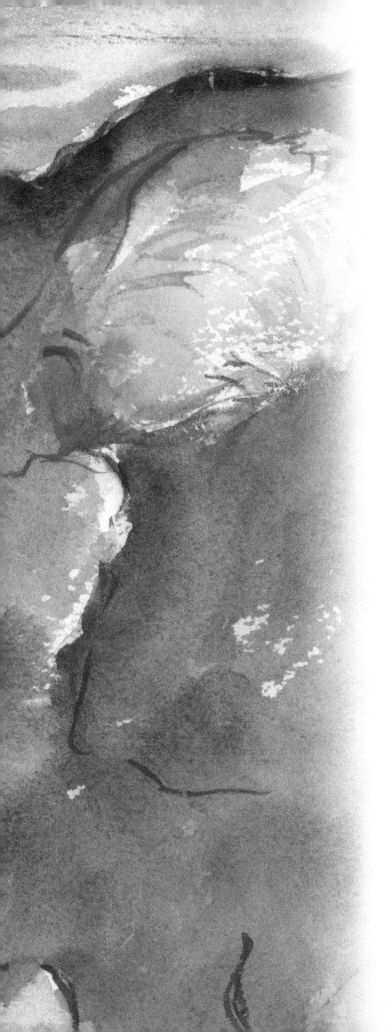

Violet had just pulled up a website on cows when she heard James laugh and say, "Cool! It feels like sandpaper covered in slime."

Violet looked up and asked, "What happened?"

James smiled and said, "I reached out my hand and the cow licked it!"

Violet realized that if she hadn't moved out of line to look up cows online, the real cow would have licked her hand instead.

They went to look at the sheep pen next. There were many mommy and baby sheep. Ms. Fannie said the moms are called ewes and the babies are called lambs. The farmers shear the wool off to make yarn to sell at the farm store. Violet wanted to see more pictures of wool, so she looked up 'wool' on her tablet.

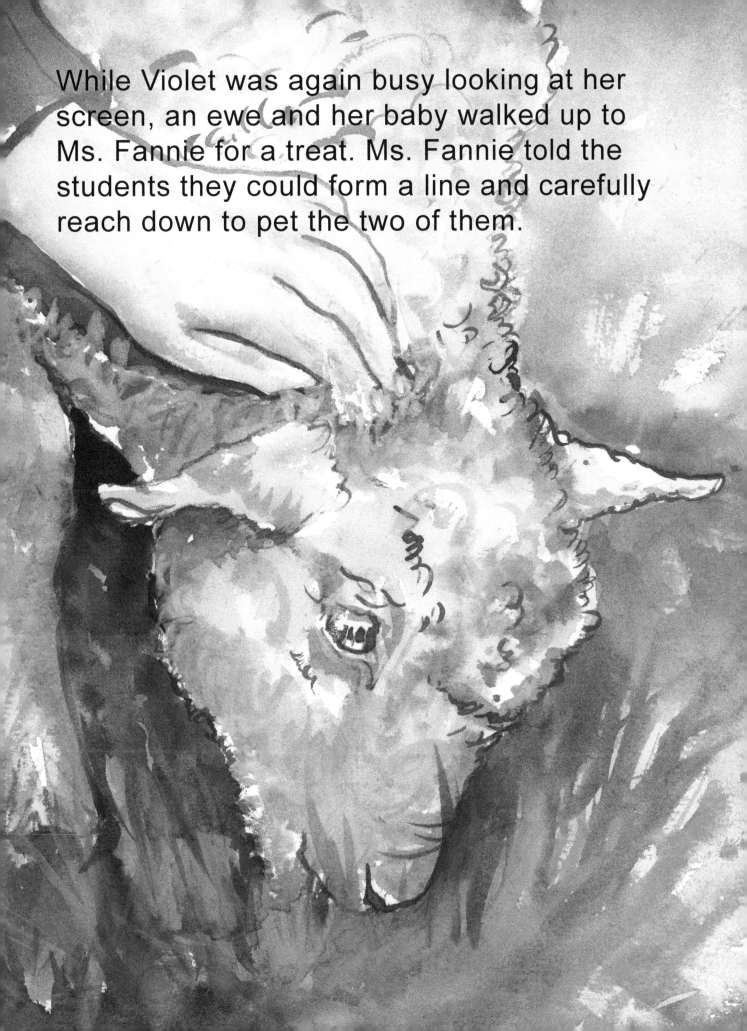

While Violet was again busy looking at her screen, an ewe and her baby walked up to Ms. Fannie for a treat. Ms. Fannie told the students they could form a line and carefully reach down to pet the two of them.

Violet looked up from her tablet and saw the line to pet the soft sheep. She was the last in line. Just before she got her turn, the ewe and lamb ran off to be with the rest of the herd.

Violet didn't get a chance to feel the soft wool.

Ms. Fannie led the class to a field with rows of carrots and strawberries planted in the ground. She was talking about how they grow the fruits and vegetables to sell them at the farm. Ms. Fannie continued talking while Violet decided to look up strawberries on her tablet. Strawberries were Violet's favorite fruit.

Violet looked up after a few minutes to see that her class had separated into two groups, so she went with the closest one. She followed as her group walked down one path, and the other students went the opposite direction. Ms. Fannie told her group that they got to pick a carrot from the row they were standing by. She showed them how to pull one up.

Violet looked across the field to see the other students picking strawberries. She raised her hand in the air and asked, "Ms. Fannie, can I go to the group over by the strawberries?"

"I'm sorry, but no. I can't have anybody accidentally walk on the plants. That is why I had you get into the group you wanted from the beginning," replied Ms. Fannie.

Violet hadn't heard the directions, so she missed her chance to eat farm fresh strawberries.

This field trip had not turned out how Violet thought it would. She missed seeing the baby chicks, feeling the cow's tongue, petting the ewe and lamb, and eating her favorite fruit.

At home, Violet's mom asked about the field trip. Violet told her she had discovered some things are better to learn in person than through a tablet. The next time her class plans to go on a field trip, she vowed to leave her tablet at home.

CPSIA information can be obtained
at www.ICGtesting.com
Printed in the USA
LVHW070806040720
659721LV00014B/1815